THE YEAR SANTA WENT MODERN

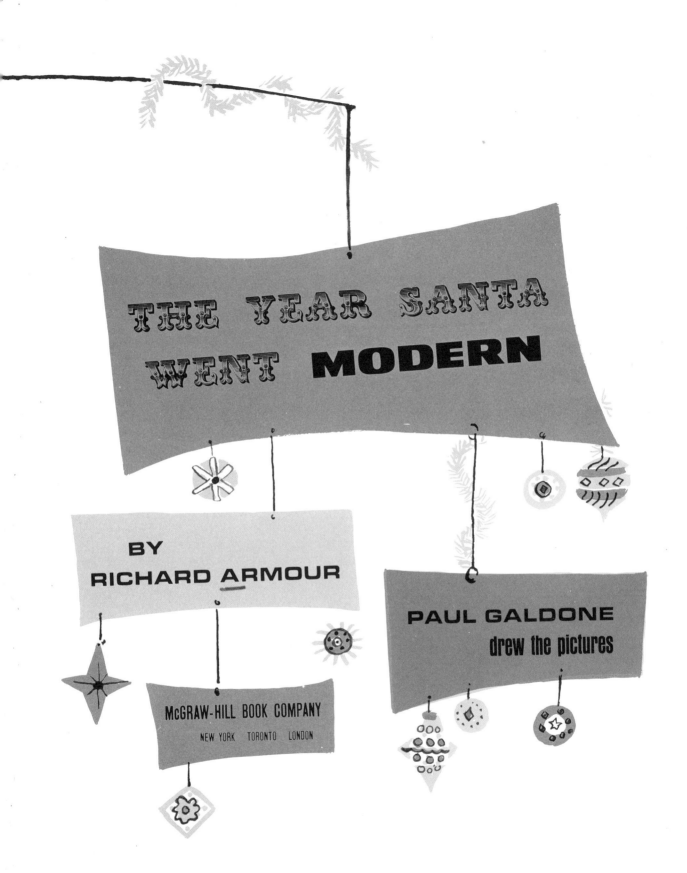

THE YEAR SANTA WENT MODERN

BY
RICHARD ARMOUR

PAUL GALDONE
drew the pictures

McGRAW-HILL BOOK COMPANY

NEW YORK   TORONTO   LONDON

Though Santa Claus is a white-haired fellow,
He isn't old, he is only mellow.
How he got to look as he does is a mystery,
Unknown, for sure, by the writers of history.
Some say he turned white
In a single night,
But others insist,
"No, that isn't right,
He was stout from the start, with a middle-aged spread,
And a little bit chubby from toe to head,
Helped along by the reindeer milk he's been reared on,
And of this we are sure:
He was born with his beard on."
Santa keeps no clocks anywhere around
That have to be set and have to be wound,
But only a calendar so he'll remember
When it's the twenty-fifth
Day of December.

5

Well, so things went, until one fine day
(Or was it so fine?—it is hard to say),
When a helper of Santa's, an elf named Slick,
Came up to Santa and said, "Saint Nick,
I—er—I'm sorry to mention this, but,"
And then, gaining courage, "We're in a rut."
"Continue," said Santa, for though it sounded
Uncomplimentary, rude, and unfounded,
Santa was never the kind to grow furious,
Or even annoyed, and he *was* quite curious.

"It's this way," said Slick, as he twisted his cap,
And picked up the button that dropped in his lap,
"We're shipping our sugarplums, bicycles, toys
On time every Christmas
To girls and to boys.
I've heard no complaints, but," and here he grew
Quivery,
"I'm frankly ashamed of our means of delivery.
We're still using reindeer and old-fashioned sleigh
As they did in my father's
And grandfather's day.
Yes, still we go hippety, hippety, hoppety,
Hoof upon roof-
Top, clippety-cloppety,
Though Donder might wonder and Blitzen might yelp,
There are times power steering
And braking would help."

His say being said, and a bit heavyhearted,
For he doubted improvement, poor Slick then departed,
And left Santa wondering . . . "Maybe he's right,
For Slick, though he's pushy,
Is clever and bright.
He's risen to foreman amongst many elves,
In charge of the uppermost candy-cane shelves.
Yes, he's right and I'm left—far behind, out-of-date."
Then he said, with a smile, "But it isn't too late.
I'll show them" (his cheeks, which had paled, were now ruddy)

"I'm as modern as any,
No old fuddy-duddy.". .

Shortly after, in answer to letters he'd written,
Came dropping like raindrops, as quick as a kitten,
All manner of magazines,
Catalogues, mailings,
Sent by train
And by plane
And by steamship sailings,
Addressed: "Mr. Claus, No. 1 North Pole,"
With a note to the postman:
"Run, don't stroll."

9

And Santa for days studied part and particle
Of every single (and double) article.
He didn't tell Dasher or Dancer or Vixen,
Prancer, Cupid, or Comet, or Donder and Blitzen,
But what he was pondering (just between *us*)
Was some sort of motor bike, auto, or bus
To buy C.O.D. from the city it's made in,
With a slightly used sleigh and eight reindeer as trade-in.

10

"Now this might be it," figured Santa, his finger
A-point at a picture and stopping to linger.
"I could circle the chimney
At Johnsons' and Warners',
I even could square it
Without cutting corners.
I could climb steepest roof-tops,
From shingle to shingle."
He shivered with pleasure,
With pleasure a-tingle.
Then he looked once again at this novel contraption
And read
What it said
Underneath, in the caption:
"GOLF CART, capacity four bags of clubs,
Two players may ride it, good golfers or dubs."

"*Hmm,*" he thought to himself, as quick as a wink
(To himself the sole way he could think of to think),
"There's a nice place for carrying presents, I see,
And room up in front for a helper and me.
But with jackknives to sharpen
And marbles to polish,
With dolls to put heads on,
Both large ones and smallish,
I haven't the leisure—no ifs, ands, or buts,—
To be out taking lessons and practicing putts.
No," Santa continued, "it wouldn't be fair—
No golfing, no golf cart.
That's final.
So there!"

Next he looked at a scooter
Imported from Italy,
That not only scooted
But tooted "Tum-*ti*-ta-lee."
But this he discarded as being too small,
With no room for presents,
No room at all.

He looked then at sports cars,
Long, sleek, and low-built
For turning a corner while going full tilt,
And one he quite liked—it was Christmasy red—
But *could* he get in without hitting his head?
Could he sit in a crouch
And a slouch
As required,
And not twist his back
And get terribly tired?
"Sports cars are fine for the supple of spine,"
Sighed Santa, "but not
For old bones like mine."

He also considered, in manner extensive,
Both prop planes and jets, which he found quite expensive,
And hard to take off from the ice and the snow in
And harder to stop, or go cautiously slow in.

Helicopter? At first that would seem just the ticket,
To whir off straight up and to land on a picket.
But Santa said, "No, though it *would* be of service,
That propeller above me would make me too nervous."

16

Santa toyed with the thought of a large station wagon,
With plenty of room to store many a bag in,
With top not too low
And with speed not too high,
And snow tires to get
A good grip on the sky.

But those tires made him think about what he had not
Thought about in some time, and in fact had forgot:
To wit, of his reindeer,
To wit, of his sleigh.
(He was feeling too witty for words today.)
"A sleigh," Santa mused, "has no tires and no punctures,
Which come, very oft, at embarrassing junctures.
And reindeer will start in the coldest of weather,
And tirelessly tug on the sleigh-pulling tether.
They may sway, they may swerve (they've their nerve),
They may balk, too,
But they're surer to get there
And better to talk to."

So Santa decided to overrule Slick
And to old-fashioned sleigh and to reindeer to stick
For safety and comfort—yes, even survival,
But mostly, come Christmas, for on-time arrival.

"And yet," Santa mused, as he peered at his mirror,
"I'll have to admit I look queerer
And queerer.
No doubt I'm outmoded,
Outdistanced, outdone,
By just about"—(tears filled his eyes)—
"Everyone."

Then he brightened.   For Santa was never long sad.
By nature, you see, he was bubbly and glad,
And also too busy, with Christmas-time coming,
For tears of self-pity, and glooming and glumming.
He glanced at the mirror that stood on the shelf. . . .
"I'll keep the old sleigh, but I'll streamline myself!
I've let myself go.
I'm not plump—let's not twiddle—
I'm F-A-T, fat,
Would you look at that middle!"

He cut out the starches,
He cut out the candy,
Though the sweet-tooth he had
Was a double-dyed dandy.
No pies did he eat, not a slice, and no cakes.
When reaching for pastry, he put on the brakes.
He gave up all foods that had given him fun
And counted the calories

One

By

One

One day, just by chance, he walked nearer and nearer,
Then wham! stood in front of a head-to-toe mirror.
He saw his reflection and let out a cry:
"Is that me?"
Then correcting himself,
"Is that I?"
His Santa Claus suit, as he stood there all gapery,
Hung loose as a bathrobe or toga or drapery,
All shapeless and sagging and no place to pin it,
With room for three elves and a reindeer within it.

"Good gracious!" cried Santa,
And "Bad gracious!" too.
"Just look at this outfit.
Now what shall I do?
Nothing fits any more
But my cap and my boots,
And I've nothing to wear
Save these oversized suits."

So he summoned his tailors, said "Drop all your pleasures!
Come quick with your shears and your thread and your measures.
I'm too small for my britches and jacket, you'll see,
Or my britches and jacket are too big for me."
Six bowlegged tailor-elves came at his call,
And with them came Slick, who had started it all.

But Santa no sooner had said,
"Cut it down,"
Than he saw on Slick's face (and where else?)
A big frown.
"What's troubling you, Slick?"
Santa asked.   "Can't they whittle
And trim my suit down,
Here and there, just a little?
As they sew, they shall rip,
As they rip, they shall sew.
Let 'er rip!" to the tailors he said.
"Now let's go."

"Forgive me, dear Santa," said Slick. "I'm aware
You're keeping your sleigh and your reindeer, but spare,
Oh, spare us the sight of that Santa Claus suit.
It's horribly dated, it's not even cute.
Why not, now your figure is youthfully sharp,
Shaped more like a flute
Than a drum or a harp,
Wear clothes that both fit and befit you—I mean
The kind with a line that is tapered and lean?"
Well, Slick was persuasive and Santa gave in.
"Go ahead, boys," he said to the tailors.
"You win."

The shears whicked and whacked,
The needles flew fast,
Threads threaded their way
Until *presto!*—at last
There was Santa, attired like the fashion world's greatest,
In a chipper checked suit that was later than latest.
It had tiny lapels
And just the right taper.
(Slick had spotted the style
In a Paris newspaper.)
In a tab-collar shirt
With a narrow silk tie,
Santa looked as sharp
As a sparrow's eye.
And on top of his head, as a final spangle,
Was a hat
That sat
At a rakish angle:
A low-tapered crown with a brim no wider
Than the span of the hips of a half-starved spider.

But Slick said, unsatisfied, "Santa, you're weird,
In that up-to-date outfit
And out-of-date beard."

Santa stood looking, his mouth wide ajar,
Then said, "Since I've already gone this far,
Please hand me my razor, my brush, and my soap,
And stand aside, everyone, please—
And hope!"

Off whiskers from left side
And off from the right,
Off under the nose,
Off the chin—what a sight!
For there, now clean-shaven, his face round and rosy,
Stood Santa, his cheeks smooth as petals of posy.
A young face it was, without wrinkle or line,
And of age not a single revealing sign.

Then suddenly Santa, who had a good view
Of himself as he stood there—
The modern, the new,
The whiskerless, slim,
Continentally clothed—
Had a thought that the instant he had it he loathed,
And he glanced at the calendar, noticed the day:
Christmas was only a week away!

Here is the thought Santa had: "When I show me
At Christmas, like this,
Will anyone know me?
I might, if I carry a brief case, be taken
For salesman or tax man, be wholly forsaken
By people who think, and they've no way of telling,
I'm either collecting for something
Or selling.
After all, I'm a symbol, an honored tradition.
I've a steady job and an annual mission.
Many things change—and they should,
For that matter—
But some things just don't,
And I'm one of the latter."

But how, in the week that remained (it was late),
No matter how much and how quickly he ate,
Could he fill his oversized Santa Claus outfit
So it would fit
Or even about fit?
More difficult still, pray how in the world
Could his whiskers grow back and be long and curled
In a single week
On cheek
And on chin
That were bare
Of hair
As an empty bin?

The answer is that it couldn't be done,
Not by Santa Claus or by anyone.

But Santa did what he had to do,
Even as I
And even as you.
That year when he traveled all over the earth
Spreading Christmas presents and cheer and mirth,
Spreading Christmas presents and mirth and cheer
From an old-fashioned sleigh drawn by eight reindeer
(Slick, if you wonder,
No longer was foreman,
But had been demoted
To back-door doorman),
Santa wore a false beard that you'd think was real
And that felt real, too, if you chanced to feel,
And into his waist, where he'd grown so small,
He rolled up a pillow as round as a ball. . . .

But the next year, I think it ought to be known,
His beard and his tummy were both his own.